THE·EIGHTIES

C000001714

PART FOUR

Production: Sadie Cook
Music processed by Global Music Solutions, Surrey SM6 9BT
Cover design by Headline Publicity Limited

Published 1997

© International Music Publications Limited
Southend Road, Woodford Green, Essex IG8 8HN, England

ALL AT ONCE

Words by JEFFREY OSBORNE and MICHAEL MASSER
Music by MICHAEL MASSER

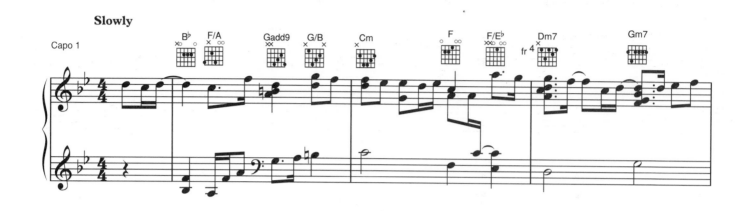

All at once

I fi- nally took a mo - ment and_ I'm re - al- iz- ing that_

6

Verse 2:
All at once
I looked around and found
That you were with another love
In someone else's arms
And all my dreams were shattered
All at once

All at once
The smile that used to greet me
Brightens someone else's day
She took your smile away
And left me with just memories
All at once

ALWAYS

Words and Music by JOHN LEWIS, DAVID LEWIS
and WAYNE LEWIS

Moderately slow

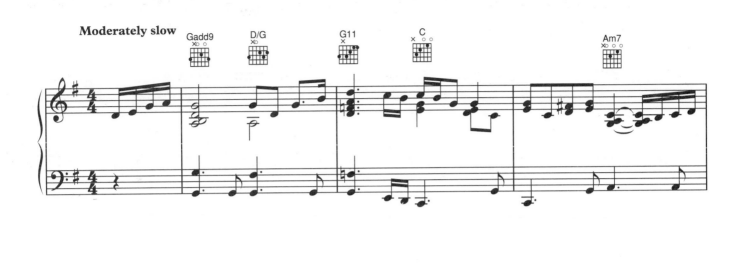

Girl you are___ to me___ all that a wo-man should be, and I
Come with me___ my sweet;___ let's go make a fa - mi - ly. And

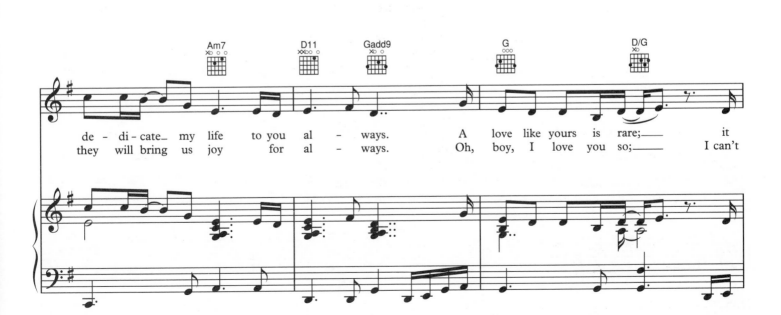

de - di - cate___ my life to you al - ways. A love like yours is rare;___ it
they will bring us joy for al - ways. Oh, boy, I love you so;___ I can't

BABY COME TO ME

Words and Music by ROD TEMPERTON

Verse 2:
Spendin' every dime to keep you talkin' on the line
That's how it was
And all those walks together
Out in any kind of weather
Just because
There's a brand new way of looking at your life
When you know that love is standing by your side

BREAKOUT

Words and Music by ANDREW CONNELL, CORINNE DREWERY
and MARTIN JACKSON

-pla - na -tions make no sense when ev - ery ans-wer's wrong.
-tu - a - tions ne - ver change to mor - row looks un - sure.

_____ You're fight - ing with lost con - fi - dence all ex-
_____ Don't leave your des - ti - ny to chance what are

-pec - ta - tions gone the time has come to make
you wait - ing for? The time has come to make

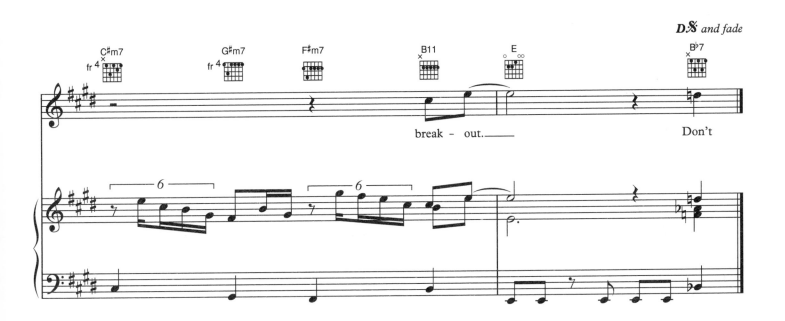

CAN'T STAY AWAY FROM YOU

Words and Music by GLORIA ESTEFAN

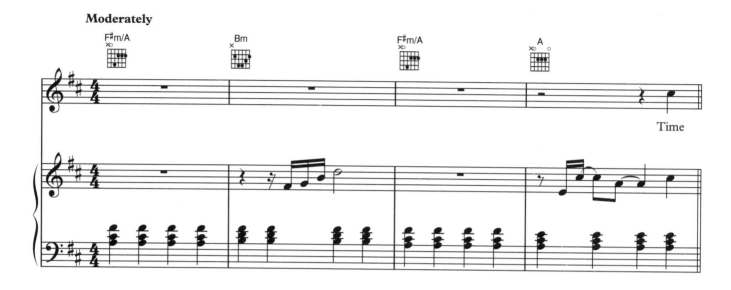

Time

flies   when you're hav - ing fun,   I heard some-bo - dy say.___
on   to   ev - ery bit___ of hope,   that's all I ev - er do,___

But if all___ I've been is fun,___   then ba - by, let___ me go.___   Don't wan-na be   in your
hop-ing you might change your mind___ and call me up___ to say___ how much   you need me

CAUGHT UP IN THE RAPTURE

Words and Music by DIANNE QUANDER and GARRY DE WAYNE GLENN

DON'T YOU WANT ME

Words and Music by PHILIP OAKEY, ADRIAN WRIGHT
and JO CALLIS

Moderately

You were

work-ing as a wait-ress in a cock-tail___ bar___   when I met   you.
(see additional lyrics)

Don't you want me ba - by, don't you want me, oh._____

repeat and fade

Verse 2:
Now five years later on you've got the world at your feet
Success has been easy for you
But don't forget it's me who put you where you are now
And I can put you back down too

Verse 3:
I was working as a waitress in a cocktail bar
That much is true
But even then I knew I'd find a much better place
Either with or without you

Verse 4:
The five years we have had have been such good times
I still love you
But now I think it's time I live my life on my own
I guess it's just what I must do

DRIVE

Words and Music by RIC OCASEK

Who's gon - na tell you when___ it's
Who's gon - na hold you down___ when

too___ late?___
you___ shake?___

EVERYTHING MUST CHANGE

Words and Music by PAUL YOUNG and IAN KEWLEY

dream, a life, a rea - son._____ Ev - ery - thing must_____ change, ev - ery - thing, ev - ery -

-thing must change_____ And like a world, this Earth and sea - sons_____ ev - ery - thing must

__ change. Ev - ery - thing, ev - ery - thing must change._____

D. 𝄋 and fade

And like a

FRIENDS WILL BE FRIENDS

Words and Music by FREDDIE MERCURY and JOHN DEACON

THE GIRL IS MINE

Words and Music by MICHAEL JACKSON

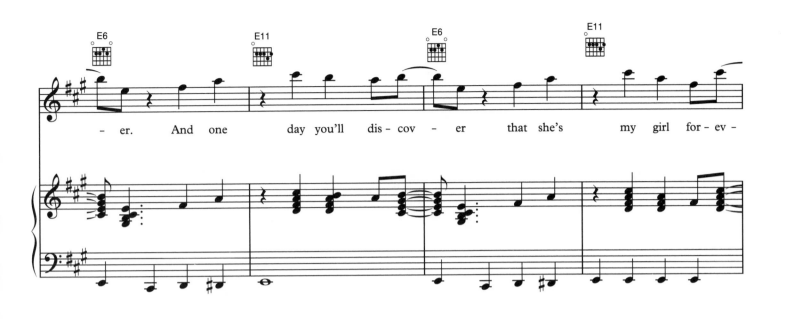

-er. And one day you'll dis - cov – er that she's my girl for - ev -

D.% *al Coda* ⊕ *CODA*

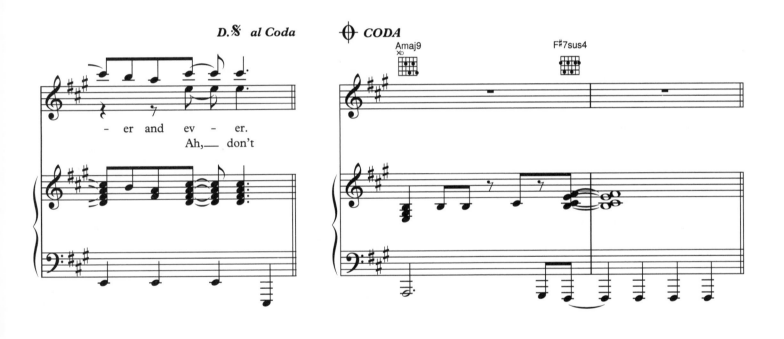

- er and ev – er.
Ah,— don't

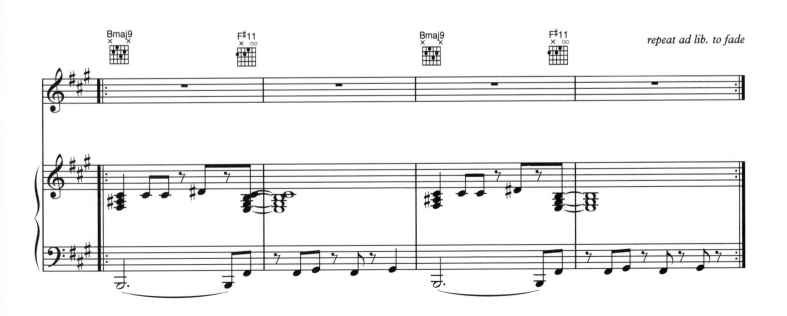

repeat ad lib. to fade

HAPPY BIRTHDAY

Words and Music by STEVIE WONDER

birth - day,_____ hap-py birth - day._____ Hap - py

Verse 2:
I just never understood
How a man who died for good
Could not have a day that would
Be set aside for his recognition
Because it should never be
Just because some cannot see
The dream as clear as he
That they should make it become an illusion
And we all know everything
That he stood for time will bring
For in peace our hearts will sing
Thanks to Martin Luther King
Happy birthday . . .

Verse 3:
The time is overdue
For people like me and you
Who know the way to truth
Is love and unity to all God's children
It should be a great event
And the whole day should be spent
In full rememberance
Of those who lived and died
For the oneness of all people
So let us all begin
We know that love can win
Let it out, don't hold it in
Sing as loud as you can
Happy birthday . . .

Recitation for fade ending:
We know the key to unity of all people
It was in the dream that we had so long ago
That lives in all of the hearts of people
That believe in unity
We will make the dream become a reality
I know we will, because our hearts tell us so

HEAVEN

Words and Music by BRYAN ADAMS and JIM VALLANCE

Oh, think-in' a - bout all our young-er years;
there was
Oh, once in your life__ you will find some-one
who will

on - ly you__ and me;__ we were young and wild__ and free.__
turn your world a - round; bring you up when you're feel - ing down..

Now no-thing can take__ you a - way from me;
we've been
Yeah, no-thing could change what you mean to me.
Oh, there's

I SHOULD HAVE KNOWN BETTER

Words and Music by JIM DIAMOND and GRAHAM LYLE

I WON'T LET THE SUN GO DOWN ON ME

Words and Music by NICHOLAS KERSHAW

Lyrics:

For-ty winks in the lob-by, make mine a G. and T. then to our fav-'rite hob-by
Mo-ther Na-ture is-n't in it, three hun-dred mil-lion years, good-bye in just a min-ute

search-ing for an e-ne-my. Here in our pa-per hou-ses, stretch-ing for miles and miles,
gone for-ev-er, no more tears. Pin-ball man, pow-er glut-ton, vac-uum in-side his head,

old men in strip-ey trou-sers rule the world with plas-tic smiles.
fore-fin-ger on the but-ton, is he blue or is he red?

Good or bad, like it or not, it's the on-ly
Break your si-lence if you would be-fore the sun goes

JAPANESE BOY

Words and Music by BOB HEATLIE

Moderately

He said that he loved me,— ne-ver would go,— oh, oh,— oh, oh.—
Peo-ple ask a-bout him, ev-e-ry day, oh, oh,— oh, oh.—

Now I find I'm sit-ting— here on my own, oh, oh,— oh, oh.— Was it some-thing
Don't know what to tell— them, what can I say,— oh, oh,— oh, oh.— If on-ly he would

KEEP ON LOVING YOU

Words and Music by KEVIN CRONIN

KIDS IN AMERICA

Words and Music by MARTY WILDE and RICKY WILDE

THE KING OF ROCK 'N' ROLL

Words and Music by PADDY McALOON

La la la la la la la la la la la la.

La la la la la la la la la la la la. All my

la - zy teen - age boasts
(see additional lyrics)

are__ now high pre - ci - sion ghosts,

and__ they're com - ing round__ the track

to

haunt me.

When she looks at me__ and laughs,

I__ re - mind her of__ the facts;

I'm__ the

Verse 2:
The dream helps you forget
You ain't never danced a step
You were never fleet of foot
Hippy
All the pathos you can keep
For the children in the street
For the vision I have had
Is weeping
New broom, this room
Sweep it clean

Verse 3:
Now my rhythm ain't so hot
But it's the only friend I've got
I'm the king of rock and roll
Completely
All the pretty birds have flown
Now I'm dancing on my own
I'm the king of rock and roll
Completely
Up from suede shoes
To my baby blues

LADY IN RED

Words and Music by CHRIS DE BURGH

I've ne-ver seen you look-ing so love-ly as you did to-night;
(see additional lyrics)

I've ne-ver seen you shine so bright. Mm mm mm.

I've ne-ver seen so ma-ny men ask you if you want-ed to dance.

It's where I wan-na be.___ But I hard-ly know___

this beau-ty by___ my side,___ I'll ne-ver for-get___

the way you look to-night.___

the way you look___ to-night.___

Verse 2:
I've never seen you looking so gorgeous as you did tonight
I've never seen you shine so bright
You were amazing
I've never seen so many people want to be there by your side
And when you turned to me and smiled
It took my breath away
I have never had such a feeling
Such a feeling of complete and utter love
As I do tonight

LAND OF MAKE BELIEVE

Words and Music by ANDY HILL and PETE SINFIELD

Freely

Stars in your eyes,— lit-tle one,— where do you go— to dream?

— To a place— we all know. The land— of make be -

moderately bright

-lieve.

moderately bright

MANIC MONDAY

Words and Music by CHRISTOPHER

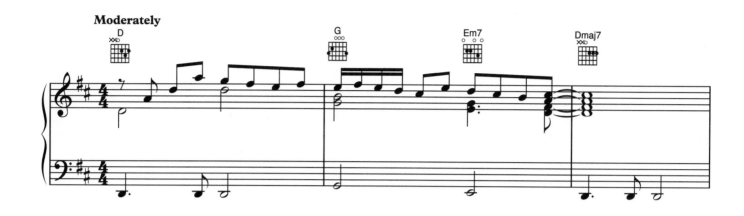

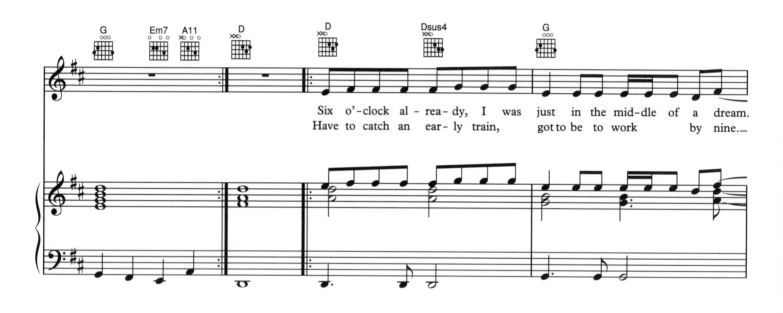

Six o'-clock al-rea-dy, I was just in the mid-dle of a dream.
Have to catch an ear-ly train, got to be to work by nine.—

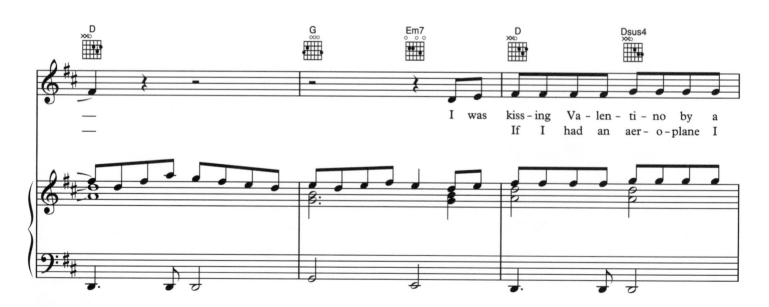

— I was kiss-ing Va-len-ti-no by a
— If I had an aer-o-plane I

MISSING YOU

Words and Music by JOHN WAITE, MARK LEONARD
and CHAS SANDFORD

Medium rock

Ev- ery time I think___ of you,___ I al- ways catch___ my breath,
name in cer-tain cir-cles, and it al- ways makes___ me smile.
know how des-perate I've be-come and it looks like I'm los-ing this fight.___

— and I'm___ still stand-ing here, and you're___ miles a - way,___ and I'm
— I spend my time think-ing___ a-bout you,___ and it's
— In your world I have no mean-ing, though I'm

MY ONE TEMPTATION

Words and Music by MICK LEESON, PETER VALE
and MILES WATERS

A NEW FLAME

Words and Music by MICK HUCKNALL

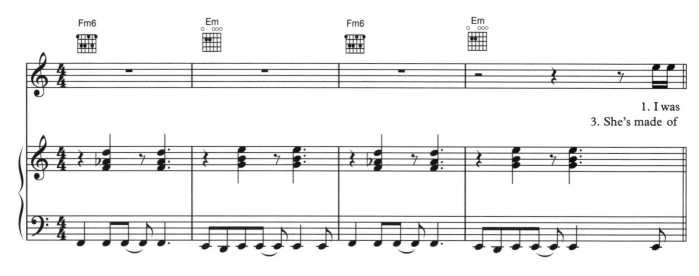

ON THE WINGS OF LOVE

Words by JEFFREY OSBORNE
Music by PETER SCHLESS

Just smile for me_ and let_ the day_ be-gin.
(see additional lyrics)

You are_ the sun-shine that lights my heart with - in._ And I'm sure that you're_ an an-

- gel in_dis-guise. Come take_ my hand and_ to - ge-ther we_will ride._

1st time only

120

fly-ing high up-on— the wings of love,—

of—— love.——

Verse 2:
You look at me and I begin to melt
Just like the snow, when a ray of sun is felt
And I'm crazy 'bout you, baby, can't you see?
I'd be so delighted if you would come with me

NINE TO FIVE

Words and Music by DOLLY PARTON

Tum-ble out of bed and stum-ble to the kitch-en; pour my-self a cup___ of am-bi-tion, and
(see additional lyrics)

yawn, and stretch, and try to come___ to life.___

Jump in the show-er and the blood stars pump-ing; out on the street, the traf-fic starts jump-ing, with folks

Verse 2:
They let you dream just to watch them shatter
You're just a step on the boss man's ladder
But you've got dreams he'll never take away
In the same boat with a lot of your friends
Waitin' for the day your ship'll come in
And the tide's gonna turn, and it's all gonna roll your way

Chorus 4 & 6:
Nine to five, they've got you where they want you
There's a better life, and you dream about it, don't you
It's a rich man's game, no matter what they call it
And you spend your life putting money in his pocket

ONE MOMENT IN TIME

Words and Music by JOHN BETTIS and ALBERT HAMMOND

126

ORINOCO FLOW

Words and Music by ENYA, NICKY RYAN
and ROMA RYAN

132

- way.—
sail,— we can sail,— sail a - way, sail a -way, sail a - way.

Sail a -

Verse 2:
From Bissau to Palau in the shade of Avalon
From Fiji to Tiree and the Isles of Ebony
From Peru to Cebu, feel the power of Babylon
From Bali to Cali far beneath the Coral Sea

Verse 3:
From the North to the South, Ebudae unto Khartoum
From the deep Sea of Clouds to the Island of the Moon
Carry me on the waves to the lands I've never been
Carry me on the waves to the lands I've never seen

SHE'S LIKE THE WIND

Words and Music by PATRICK SWAYZE and STACY WIDELITZ

She's like the wind through my tree.

She rides the night next to me. She

leads me through moon-light on-ly to burn me with the sun. She's

SAVE A PRAYER

Words and Music by SIMON LE BON, ANDY TAYLOR, ROGER TAYLOR
JOHN TAYLOR and NICK RHODES

- ter. No,— don't   say a prayer for me now;   save it for the morn-ing af-

- ter. _____

- ter. _____

SEE THE DAY

Words and Music by D C LEE

ST ELMO'S FIRE (MAN IN MOTION)

Words and Music by DAVID FOSTER and JOHN PARR

Gon na be your man in mo-tion. All I need is a pair of wheels. Take me where the fu-ture's ly-ing;

St. El- mo's fire.

St. El- mo's fire.

And my time is now; I'm com-in' a-live.

I can see a new ho-ri-zon un-der-neath the blaz-ing sky. I'll be where the ea-gle's fly-ing

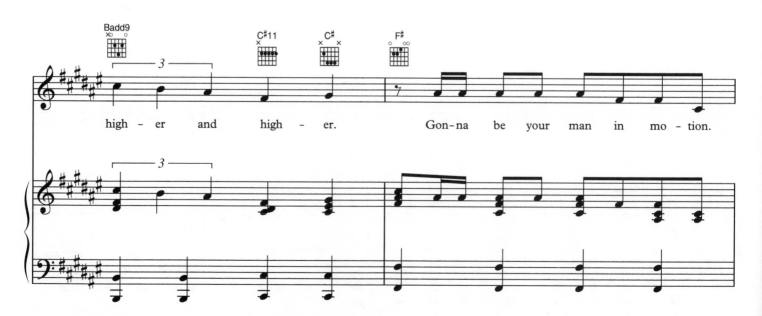

high-er and high-er. Gon-na be your man in mo-tion.

Verse 2:

Play the game; you know you can't quit until it's won
Soldier on, only you can do what must be done
You know, in some ways you're a lot like me
You're just a prisoner, and you're tryin' to break free

Verse 3:

Burning up; don't know just how far that I can go
Soon be home; only just a few miles down the road
And I can make it, I know I can
You broke the boy in me, but you won't break the man

Chorus 3:

I can hear the music playin'; I can see the banners fly
Feel like a vet again. I hope I ain't high
Gonna be your man in motion; all I need is a pair of wheels
Take me where the future's lying; St. Elmo's fire

SUPERWOMAN

Words and Music by ANTONIO REID, KENNY EDMONDS
and DARYL SIMMONS

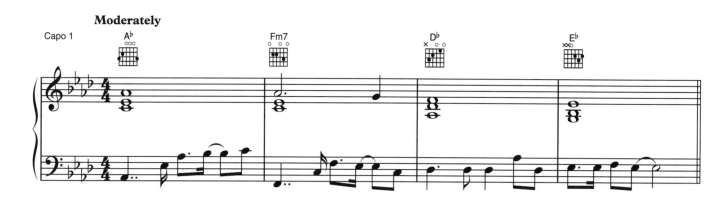

Ear - ly in the morn - ing I put break - fast at your ta - ble, and
say the juice is sour it used to be so sweet, and I
way through the rush hour try - ing to make it home just for you, I want to
think I am just cra - zy when I say that you've changed, I'm con -

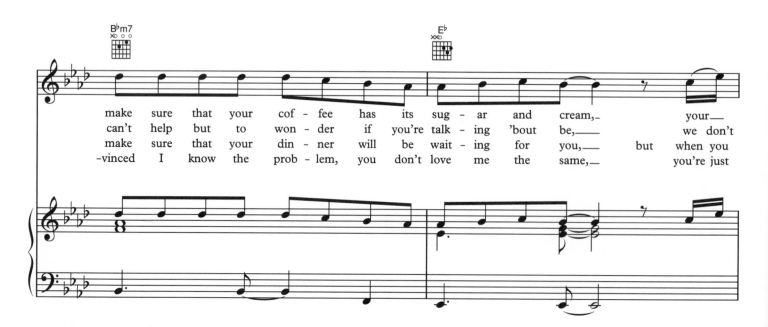

make sure that your cof - fee has its sug - ar and cream, your___
can't help but to won - der if you're talk - ing 'bout be,___ we don't
make sure that your din - ner will be wait - ing for you,___ but when you
-vinced I know the prob - lem, you don't love me the same,___ you're just

SUMMER OF '69

Words and Music by BRYAN ADAMS and JIM VALLANCE

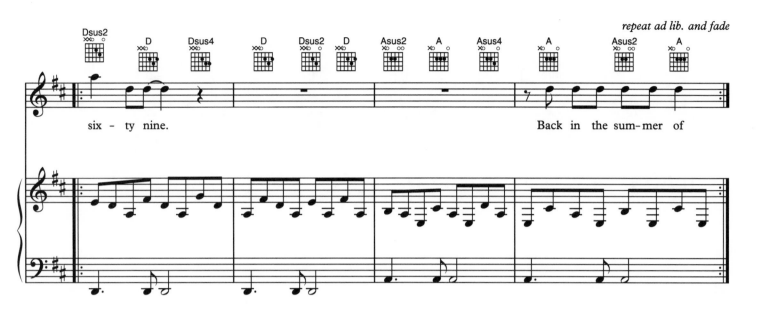

six - ty nine.

Back in the sum-mer of

Verse 2:
Ain't no use in complainin' when you got a job to do
Spent my evenin's down at the drive-in, and that's when I met you
Standin' on your mama's porch, you told me that you'd wait forever
Oh, and when you held my hand, I knew that it was now or never
Those were the best days of my life

Verse 3:
And now the times are changin'; look at everything that's come and gone
Sometimes when I play that old six-string I think about you; wonder what went wrong
Standin' on your mama's porch, you told me it'd last forever
Oh, and when you held my hand, I knew that it was now or never
Those were the best days of my life

UPSIDE DOWN

Words and Music by BERNARD EDWARDS and NILE RODGERS

165

say to thee re-spect-ful-ly.__ Up-side down you're turn-in' me.__

repeat to fade

WONDERFUL LIFE

Words and Music by COLIN VEARNCOMBE

1. Here I go_____ out to sea_____ a-gain, the
2. (see additional lyrics)
3. (Instrumental)

sun - shine fills my hair_____ and dreams hang in the

air.

(1.) Girls in the sky and in my
(2.3.) (see additional lyrics)

blue eye, you know it feels un - fair,_____

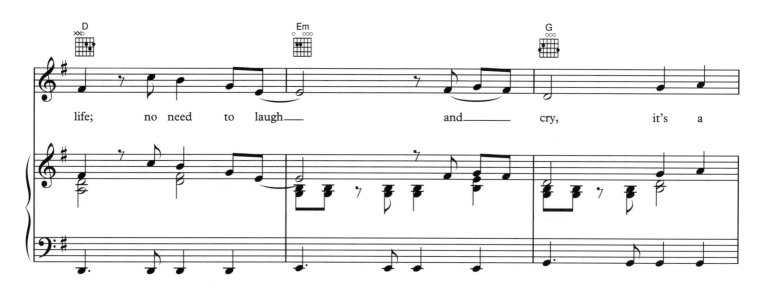

Verse 2:
The sun's in your eyes
The heat is in your hair
They seem to hate you
Because you're there
And I need a friend, oh, I need a friend
To make me happy
Not stand there on my own
Look at me standing here on my own again
Up straight in the sunshine

Verse 3:
I need a friend, oh, I need a friend
To make me happy, not so alone
Look at me here, here on my own again
Up straight in the sunshine

WAKE ME UP BEFORE YOU GO-GO

Words and Music by GEORGE MICHÆL

1999

Words and Music by PRINCE

I was dream-in' when I wrote this; for-give me if it goes a-stray,
(see additional lyrics)

but when I woke up this morn-ing, could-'ve

Nine-teen nine - ty nine.____ Don't you wan-na go? Nine - teen nine - ty nine.

repeat and fade

Verse 2:
I was dreamin' when I wrote this
So sue me if I go too fast
But life is just a party
And parties weren't meant to last
War is all around us
My mind says prepare to fight
So if I gotta die I'm gonna
Listen to my body tonight

Verse 3:
If you didn't come to party
Don't bother knockin' on the door
I've got a lion in my pocket
And, baby, he's ready to roar
Everybody's got a bomb
We could all die any day
But before I'll let that happen
I'll dance my life away

YOU BRING ME JOY

Words and Music by DAVID LASLEY

You bring me_____ joy_____ when I'm down. Oh, so much

joy._____ When I lose my way, your love comes smil-ing on me._____ I saw your

face, and then I knew we would be_____ friends._____ I was
(see additional lyrics)

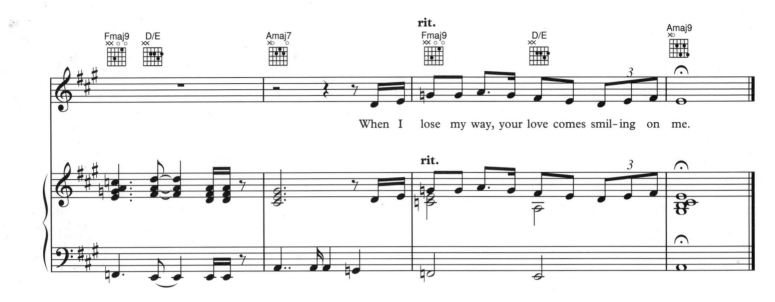

When I lose my way, your love comes smil-ing on me.

Verse 2:
You bring me joy
Don't go too far away
If I can't see your face, I will remember that smile

But can this be right
Or should we be friends?
I get lonely sometimes and I'm mixed up again
'Cause you're the best I've seen in all my life
You bring me joy
My joy, my joy

Verse3:
I believe this is gonna be what you want it to be
I just love you, I just love you, can't you see
That you're the best I've seen in all my life
You bring me joy

Printed in Great Britain by Hobbs the Printers Ltd, Totton, Hampshire 12/97